Piano
Grade 5

Pieces & Exercises
for Trinity College London exams

2015-2017

Published by
Trinity College London
www.trinitycollege.com

Registered in England
Company no. 02683033
Charity no. 1014792

Printed in England by Caligraving Ltd.

Giga in D minor

Richard Jones
(died 1744)

Capriccio in G

Domenico Scarlatti
(1685-1757)

Rondo

Third movement from Sonatina in F, op. 168

Anton Diabelli
(1781-1858)

Andantino

from Sonata on themes from *The Magic Flute*

Moritz Vogel
(1846-1922)

[Blank page to facilitate page turns]

Dedicatoria

from *Cuentos de la juventud*, op. 1

Enrique Granados
(1867-1916)

Miniature

op. 8 no. 10

Alexander Goedicke
(1877-1957)

Mister Trumpet Man

With a pronounced beat ♩ = 100

William Gillock
(1917-1993)

Spanish Dancer

from *Les Miroirs de Miró*

Edwin Roxburgh
(born 1937)

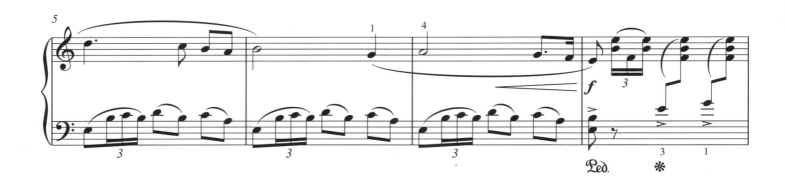

What to do when it rains

Gareth Balch
(born 1969)

Composer's original metronome mark is ♩ = 88

Exercises

1a. Waltz – tone, balance and voicing

1b. Bewildered – tone, balance and voicing

2a. Swirling – co-ordination

2b. Best Behaviour – co-ordination

3a. Dark – finger & wrist strength and flexibility

3b. Serioso – finger & wrist strength and flexibility